P9-CLA-428

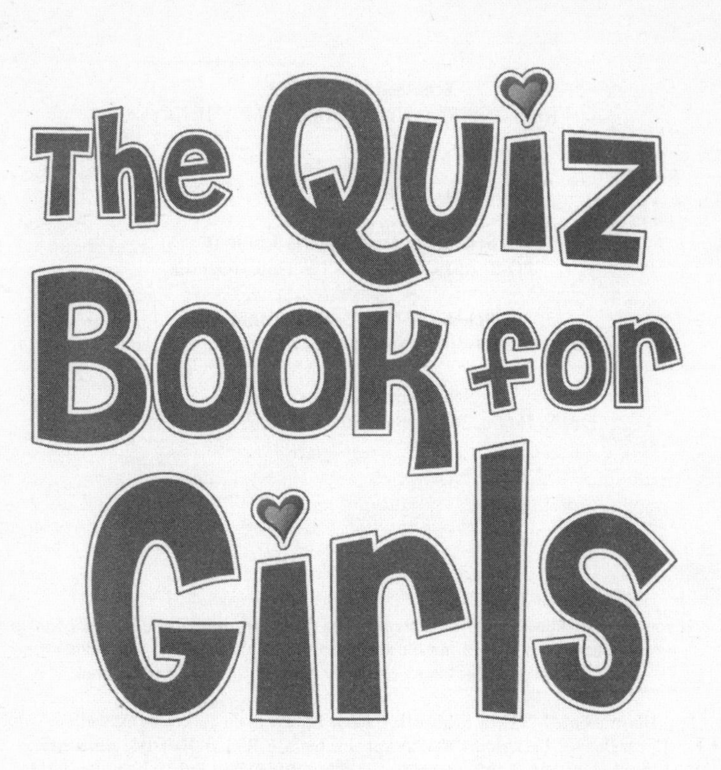

by

H. Becker

illustrations by Isabelle Charbonneau

Scholastic Canada Ltd.
Toronto New York London Auckland Sydney
Mexico City New Delhi Hong Kong Buenos Aires

Scholastic Canada Ltd.
604 King Street West, Toronto, Ontario M5V 1E1, Canada

Scholastic Inc.
557 Broadway, New York, NY 10012, USA

Scholastic Australia Pty Limited
PO Box 579, Gosford, NSW 2250, Australia

Scholastic New Zealand Limited
Private Bag 94407, Botany, Manukau 2163, New Zealand

Scholastic Children's Books
Euston House, 24 Eversholt Street, London NW1 1DB, UK

If you purchased this book without a cover, you should be aware that this book is stolen property. It was reported as "unsold and destroyed" to the publisher, and neither the author nor the publisher has received any payment for this "stripped book."

Illustrations © 2011 by Scholastic Canada Ltd., with the following exceptions: Upper Banner: background © iStockphoto.com/S-E-R-G-O, Hairstyle silhouettes © iStockphoto.com/linearcurves, Stylish silhouettes © iStockphoto.com/giraffarte; Lower Banner: © shutterstock/MisterElements; p. 62: © shutterstock/Pablo Scapinachis.

ISBN 978-1-4431-0462-3

Text copyright © 2011 by Helaine Becker
All rights reserved.

No part of this publication may be reproduced or stored in a retrieval system, or transmitted in any form or by any means, electronic, mechanical, recording, or otherwise, without written permission of the publisher, Scholastic Canada Ltd., 604 King Street West, Toronto, Ontario M5V 1E1, Canada. In the case of photocopying or other reprographic copying, a licence must be obtained from Access Copyright (Canadian Copyright Licensing Agency), 1 Yonge Street, Suite 800, Toronto, Ontario M5E 1E5 (1-800-893-5777).

6 5 4 3 2 1 Printed in Canada 121 11 12 13 14 15

TABLE OF CONTENTS

WHAT SUPERHEROINE ARE YOU?

Answer yes or no to each of the following questions:

1. I am a strong athlete and enjoy sports. no
2. I love animals of all kinds. Yes
3. I consider myself kind of geeky and smart. Yes
4. I have a secret dark side. no
5. I like to wear funky jewellery, especially bracelets. no

6. I really dig ancient civilizations. no
7. I am very future-oriented. yes
8. I can sometimes be a real drama queen. yes
9. I enjoy singing and playing musical instruments. yes
10. I love to fly but get claustrophobic in airplanes. no

Scoring

Give yourself the following points for each yes answer.

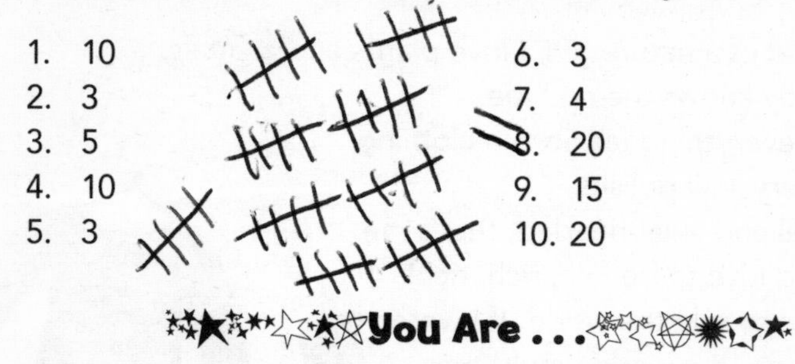

1. 10
2. 3
3. 5
4. 10
5. 3
6. 3
7. 4
8. 20
9. 15
10. 20

You Are . . .

0–10 Wonder Woman. You're the complete package — smart, charming, with talents you can draw upon in a pinch. Remember: Those boots are made for walking.

11–20 Lara Croft. Your middle name is Determination. Nothing will stand in the way of you making your dreams come true — not ancient curses, murderous mummies, nor middle school science tests. Don't forget to do your ancient Greek homework.

21–30 Xena the Warrior Princess. Yeah, female power! You are a tough competitor and can triumph even when the odds and gods are stacked against you.

31–40 Atomic Betty. Friends and family might think you are just an ordinary kid, but you know better. You are mature beyond your years. You can make the world a better place by standing up to bullies.

41+ Storm. When you walk into a room, people notice. You bring excitement wherever you go. But watch out — your temper is epic! Don't forget to kick back and chill now and then.

WHAT SUPERVILLAIN ARE YOU?

Answer yes or no to each of the following:

1. I'm kind of a nature girl. I love plants and animals.
2. Nobody knows the real me.
3. I love everything fashion — clothing, jewellery, nail polish!
4. Logical and level-headed, that's me.
5. I would love to be rich, rich, rich!
6. I'd love to rule the world. If I were in charge, the world would be a better place.
7. I am good at organizing things.
8. I get angry sometimes that the world just isn't fair.

Scoring

Give yourself the following points for each yes answer.

1. Yes 5
2. Yes 20
3. Yes 15
4. Yes 1
5. Yes 10
6. Yes 1
7. Yes 1
8. Yes 2

You Are . . .

0–9 Narnia's White Witch. Just because you are frosty through and through doesn't mean you have no feelings. You care deeply about making the world a better place . . . for snowflakes, snowmen and snow cones. (Boo, lions!)

10–20 Poison Ivy. You KNOW kryptonite is bad for the environment. So is anything silvery, plasticky or that smells like the inside of a gym bag. Ugh. Go green or go home.

21–30 Mystique. Why so blue all the time? You'll feel better if you put on some rose-coloured glasses. Or a shirt.

31–45 Cruella de Vil. You are just a wee bit crazy. Okay, a lot crazy. Your taste in clothing is something you should reconsider. Haven't you heard? Bamboo cloth is the new puppy skin.

46+ Catwoman. You are numero uno in the world of evil. You've got style, class and a killer black latex suit. You are *purr*fectly wonderful just the way you are. Now go find a litter box.

WHAT'S YOUR INNER SPORT PERSONALITY?

Are you a rough and tough hockey player deep down, or are you really a flashy steeplechase champ? Take this quiz to find out which sport represents your personal style and goals.

1. Your favourite season is . . .
   a. summer > Go to question 2.
   b. winter > Go to question 3.
   c. spring > Go to question 4.
   d. fall > Go to question 11.
2. On a super hot day, what do you prefer to do?
   a. Run through the sprinkler. > Go to question 6.
   b. Get even sweatier! > Go to question 5.
3. Which would you enjoy more?
   a. Roller coasters. > Go to question 7.
   b. Watching an exciting competition. > Go to question 8.
4. How would you describe yourself?
   a. Quick-thinking and intense. > Go to question 5.
   b. Steady, decisive, determined. > Go to question 9.
5. Which words best describe you?
   a. Traditional, conservative. > Your inner sport personality is Tennis.
   b. Independent, free-spirited. > Your inner sport personality is Beach Volleyball.
6. Large body of water: something to jump into or something to avoid?
   a. Jump in. > Your inner sport personality is Swimming.
   b. Avoid. > Your inner sport personality is Golf.

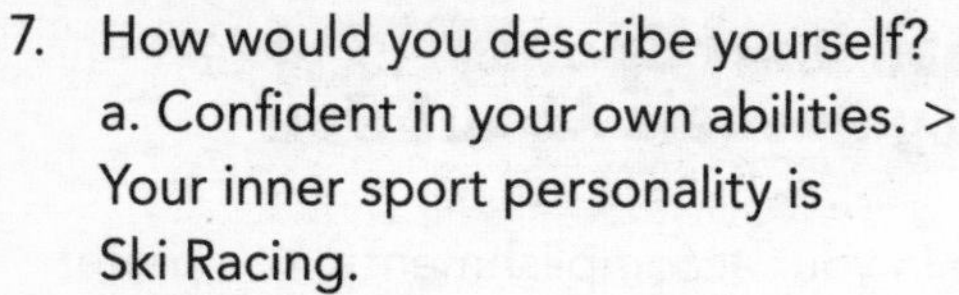

7. How would you describe yourself?
   a. Confident in your own abilities. > Your inner sport personality is Ski Racing.
   b. Trusting of others. > Your inner sport personality is Luge.
   c. Artistic. > Your inner sport personality is Figure Skating.

8. You prefer to . . .
   a. be part of a group activity. > Go to question 10.
   b. do independent activities. > Go to question 7.
9. When taking a long car trip, what do you do to pass the time?
   a. Enjoy watching the passing scenery. > Your inner sport personality is Cycling.
   b. Play on a personal game system. > Your inner sport personality is Soccer.
   c. Figure out the best route there. > Your inner sport personality is Baseball.
10. Which do you prefer?
    a. Hot cocoa. > Your inner sport personality is Hockey.
    b. Ice-cold pop. > Your inner sport personality is Basketball.
11. When you grow up, you'd like to be . . .
    a. rich. > Go to question 12.
    b. happy. > Your inner sport personality is Martial Arts.
12. Are you crazy about animals?
    a. Yes. > Your inner sport personality is Horseback Riding.
    b. I like them, but I'm more of a people person. > Your inner sport personality is Track and Field.
    c. Not too much. > Your inner sport personality is Gymnastics.

What Your Sport Personality Reveals About You

Baseball. You take pride in your accomplishments. You prefer the simple things in life — hot dogs, apple pie and good times with your pals.

Basketball. You're smart and quick on your feet. People look up to you.

Beach Volleyball. You sure know how to keep them guessing! You are the mystery woman, the gal with the half smile who won't share the joke. That's because you think life is a riot, and you're having the most fun of anyone.

Cycling. You are tough as nails, able to withstand any kind of hardship to attain your goals. Sometimes you wind up spinning your wheels. Make a road plan and stick to it.

Figure Skating. You love being the centre of attention. You have a lot of flair and a dramatic streak. You also have enormous physical and emotional strength.

Golf. You have an inner maturity that allows you to find beauty in unexpected places — the curve of a swan's back, sun dancing on water. Your success in life is all but assured.

Gymnastics. You are open-minded and flexible. You're tough and resilient, too, so life's challenges won't throw you off balance.

Hockey. You are a hard worker, determined to reach your goals no matter what. You're not afraid to take chances.

Horseback Riding. You love nature and animals, but you also have a taste for luxury. You have a soft heart, but you tend to hide it from others. You like to horse around with your friends.

Luge. You're something of a daredevil, willing to try just about anything if it sounds like fun!

Martial Arts. You are a deep thinker and enjoy quiet contemplation. You dislike confrontation but won't shy away from speaking up if you have to. You respect authority.

Ski Racing. You love adventure, and you get bored with routine. Let someone else look after the day-to-day — you've got places to go and people to meet!

Soccer. You are passionate and intense. You can be argumentative but are also generous, a real team player. Sometimes you need a kick in the pants to get going.

Swimming. Still waters run deep. You know how to stick with a problem until you solve it. You are calm but intense — beneath your cool exterior, there's a deep pool of emotion.

Tennis. You are serious and somewhat shy but a loyal and trustworthy friend. Fairness is very important to you. Remember: Life is all about the give and take.

Track and Field. You are extremely versatile. You can excel at whatever you try. Don't let life's hurdles get you down.

HOW FAIR ARE YOU?

1. Your best friend got in an argument with another girl. You . . .
   a. take her side. That's what friends are for.
   b. wait to hear the other side of the story before getting involved.
   c. listen to your friend's story carefully to try and figure out what happened.
2. A new friend asks you for help with her homework. When you get to her house, you discover she really wants you to do the homework for her! You . . .
   a. say no, even though she won't want to be friends with you anymore.
   b. do it for her. It's just this once.
   c. offer again to help her, but tell her you won't do it by yourself. Then sit down and help get her started on it.
3. Your brother or sister walked the dog yesterday. Today it's your turn. You . . .
   a. try to get out of it by pretending you have too much homework.
   b. take the dog to the park.
   c. try to talk your sib into doing it again. You're bigger than he/she is.
4. You won the school raffle! When you take a closer look at the winning ticket, you realize it actually belongs to someone else — they got mixed up. You . . .
   a. keep the prize — what she doesn't know won't hurt her.
   b. keep the prize — because you wouldn't know how to fess up without feeling foolish.
   c. Give the prize to the real winner.

5. There's one last slice of yummy cake on the kitchen counter. You know your gran hasn't had a piece. You've had two already. You . . .
   a. eat it up before anyone else does.
   b. cut a tiny slice off of it and leave the rest for Gran.
   c. would never dream of eating the last piece!
6. You are the referee in a big tennis match. You called a shot "out," but now you realize you made a mistake. Will you . . .
   a. let the call stand? You'll make a call in that player's favour later to even things up.
   b. stop the play, admit your mistake and replay the point?
   c. ignore it? Everyone makes mistakes sometimes. It will all work out in the end.

Scoring

1. a3 b1 c2
2. a1 b3 c2
3. a3 b1 c3
4. a3 b2 c1
5. a3 b2 c1
6. a3 b1 c2

You Are . . .

6–10 Fairest in the land. You think it's important to do the right thing all the time, even when it's uncomfortable. That's what people like about you — they know they can count on you for honest answers and fair play.

11–14 The compromiser. It's all so confusing. You hate hurting other people's feelings. But when you try to be totally objective, someone often winds up angry. So you try to find the solutions that will make everyone happy. You feel best when you follow your heart.

15–18 No fair! For you, it's more about loyalty than about right or wrong. You stick with your friends no matter what. And everyone knows you have to fight to get your fair share in this world, or you're flat out of luck. Or are you?

ARE YOU A QUEEN BEE?

1. When you get angry, what do you tend to do?
   a. Sulk in your room.
   b. Take it out on someone else.
   c. Take a deep breath, put on a happy face and wait for it to pass.
2. You're hanging in the schoolyard with your buddies. A girl you don't know is watching you. What do you do?
   a. Invite her to join you.
   b. Ignore her.
   c. Wonder what she thinks about you.

3. In general, you . . .
   a. feel good about yourself.
   b. wish you could be somebody else.
   c. have your ups and downs, just like everyone else.
4. Have you ever been bullied?
   a. No.
   b. Yes.

5. At home, how are you treated?
   a. With respect and affection.
   b. Spoiled rotten!
   c. Okay, I guess — like a kid.
6. You frequently find your school work . . .
   a. too easy.
   b. a drag.
   c. a struggle.
7. How do you feel most of the time?
   a. Happy, cheerful, optimistic.
   b. Sad, angry, irritable.
   c. Sometimes happy, sometimes sad — every day is different.
8. You are doing a group project. You . . .
   a. do your part without much fuss.
   b. divide up the tasks evenly for everyone and get to work right away.
   c. make jokes and fool around.
9. You see some kids picking on a younger girl in the schoolyard. What do you do?
   a. Call a teacher over to help.
   b. Join in.
   c. Stay away.
10. Your friend got a glittery hairband that you think is really pretty. You want to trade her a cute purse you got for your birthday. She doesn't want to. What do you do?
   a. Forget about it.
   b. Give her the cold shoulder until she gives in.
   c. Sweeten the deal by offering her some glitter pens or frosty lip gloss to keep in the purse.

Scoring

1. a2 b3 c1
2. a1 b3 c2
3. a1 b3 c2
4. a0 b3
5. a1 b3 c2
6. a2 b3 c1
7. a1 b3 c2
8. a1 b3 c3
9. a1 b3 c2
10. a1 b3 c2

9–13 You are fair-minded and democratic, more like a prime minister than a queen bee!

14–21 Sometimes you can 'bee' a bit of a princess, especially if you are tired or in a bad mood. Bee-ing aware of your feelings will help you stay sweet as honey.

22–30 Do you hear that buzzing sound? Queen bees are natural leaders, but sometimes they mistake leadership for power. If this is you, make sure you treat others like royalty, too!

WHICH KIDS' BOOK CHARACTER ARE YOU?

1. You prefer . . .
   a. rhyming poetry. > Go to question 2.
   b. chapter books. > Go to question 3.
   c. fables featuring funny animals. > Go to question 9.
2. Which word describes you best?
   a. Diva! > Go to question 4.
   b. Clown. > Go to question 5.
   c. Angel. > Go to question 6.
   d. Storyteller. > Go to question 8.
   e. Independent. > Go to question 10.
3. Do you consider yourself . . .
   a. young at heart? > Go to question 7.
   b. wise beyond your years? > Go to question 12.
4. Your favourite item of clothing is . . .
   a. shoes. > Go to question 14.
   b. funky hats or hair ornaments. > Go to question 10.
   c. cool eyeglasses. > Go to question 8.
   d. All of the above! > You are Fancy Nancy.
5. Which do you prefer to do?
   a. Organize things. > You are Amelia Bedelia.
   b. Try something new. > You are Judy Moody.
6. You believe . . .
   a. in Santa Claus. > You are Cindy Lou Who.
   b. in unicorns and other magical beings. > Go to question 11.
   c. only in what you can see and touch. > Go to question 5.

7. When you grow up, you'd like to be . . .
   a. an actor. > Go to question 13.
   b. a detective. > Go to question 15.
8. Who would you more like to have as a friend?
   a. Mary, Mary, Quite Contrary. > You are Mother Goose.
   b. A boy with a pet monkey. > You are Madeline.
9. Where would you prefer to spend an afternoon?
   a. On a farm. > Go to question 14.
   b. In the woods. > You are Scaredy Squirrel.
10. Which would you be more likely to do in an emergency?
    a. Call for help. > You are Rapunzel.
    b. Save the day. > You are the Paper Bag Princess.
11. Which treat would you prefer?
    a. Honey on toast. > You are Matilda.
    b. Jelly beans. > You are Hermione Granger.
12. When you grow up, you'd prefer to . . .
    a. ride a camel across Mongolia. > You are Miss Rumphius.
    b. visit London, England. > You are Mother Goose.
13. You like to think you are . . .
    a. a good planner. > You are Amazing Grace.
    b. imaginative. > You are Anne of Green Gables.
    c. fun to be around. > You are Ramona Quimby.
14. Which description sounds more like you?
    a. Always on the go, go, go! > You are Olivia.
    b. A logical clear thinker. > You are Charlotte the spider.

15. Which appeals to you more?
    a. Working with friends. > You are Nancy Drew.
    b. Working on your own. > You are Harriet the Spy.

You Are . . .

Amazing Grace. You have a flair for the dramatic. The stage is the place for you! You are also brave and won't take no for an answer.

Amelia Bedelia. You are creative. Your sense of humour is wacky. You love rhymes.

Anne of Green Gables. You sometimes leap before you look, but that just makes life more fun! Your favourite colour? Green. Your favourite country? CANADA!

Charlotte the spider. You are very, very clever and excellent at writing and weaving.

Cindy Lou Who. You are naturally sweet and can melt the heart of even the meanest Grinch. Try a new hairdo.

Fancy Nancy. You love glamour, dressing up and being the centre of attention. Nothing is too good for you, dahling.

Harriet the Spy. You are curious about people. You love secrets, codes and keeping a private journal. You don't like to follow rules.

Hermione Granger. Cleverness is your middle name. You are a good student, a loyal friend and an excellent speller.

Judy Moody. You can roll your tongue like a hot dog bun. You love adventure. You are independent and fun, fun, fun!

Madeline. You love french fries. You expect other people to toe the line. Your favourite colours? Blue and yellow. Your favourite animal? Babar the Elephant.

Matilda. You hate injustice. You have the power to change the world!

Miss Rumphius. You want to make the world a better place and have the guts and determination to do it.

Mother Goose. You love making people laugh. You are wise beyond your years.

Nancy Drew. You are always keen to solve a mystery or draw a picture.

Olivia. You are full of energy and can be somewhat pig-headed.

The Paper Bag Princess. You are a can-do kind of girl. Patience is for other people — you take action!

Ramona Quimby. Trouble seems to follow you wherever you go. No problem! You just kick it into the corner.

Rapunzel. You have a mind of your own. You like solitude and combing your hair. You are not afraid of heights.

Scaredy Squirrel. You have overcome your tendency toward shyness by finding a few friends who are just as nutty as you.

WHAT COLOUR IS YOUR AURA?

Which colour best reflects your inner spiritual nature? For each set of words, choose the set that best describes you.

1. a. Active, adventurous, outgoing. > Go to question 2.
   b. Responsible, goal-oriented, helpful. > Go to question 3.
   c. Imaginative, creative, idealistic. > Go to question 8.
2. a. Competitive, hard-working. > Go to question 4.
   b. Ambitious, logical. > Go to question 5.
3. a. Generous, easy-going, talkative. > Go to question 6.
   b. Sensitive, organized, kind. > Go to question 7.
4. a. Strong, physically fit. > You are Scarlet.
   b. Innovative, a leader. > You are Crimson.
5. a. Daring, productive. > You are Orange.
   b. Precise, scientific. > You are Gold.
6. a. Creative, playful. > You are Yellow.
   b. Informative, helpful. > You are Green.
7. a. Determined, mature, ambitious. > You are Sage Green.
   b. Compassionate, calm, animal lover. > You are Blue.
   c. Caring, deep thinker, spiritual. > You are White.
8. a. Artistic, intuitive. > You are Violet.
   b. Gentle, whimsical, free spirit. > You are Lilac.

What the Colour of Your Aura Means

Blue. People with blue auras love to help others. They gravitate toward professions like veterinarian, social worker or caregiver.

Crimson. People with crimson auras are natural leaders. They have lots of good ideas and are the ones who can inspire others to make them come true. Crimson people tend to do well in politics, entertainment and finance.

Gold. If you have a golden aura, you are logical, analytical and strong-minded. Science and math are areas where you excel. Astronauts, oceanographers and computer programmers tend to have golden auras.

Green. This is the teacher aura. People with green auras love to guide others and share information. They are very outgoing and make excellent hostesses and leaders.

Lilac. The lilac aura signifies a sense of freedom and whimsy. If you are a lilac, you will be creative, light-hearted and pleasure-loving. Musicians, movie stars and models tend to have lilac auras.

Orange. Orange people are the movers and shakers of the world. They are fun to be around and tend to be highly productive and successful. Look for orange auras in school council presidents and team captains.

Sage Green. If your aura is sage green, you are a quick thinker with a deep sense of responsibility. You are very well organized and ambitious, a combo that will lead you to success in the field of your choice.

Scarlet. You are strong, both physically and mentally. You have the stamina to see projects through and prefer to act rather than reflect. Scarlet people are natural athletes, explorers and business executives.

Violet. People with violet auras tend to be imaginative, expressive and artistic. Graphic artists, writers and actors all use their special skills to communicate and share their deep feelings with others.

White. The classic healer's aura. People with white auras tend to be deeply spiritual and help others find wellness through physical and spiritual means. Doctors, nurses and clergy all tend to have white auras.

Yellow. A yellow aura is the sign of popularity. Yellow people are easy to get along with and are good company. Warm hearts and sunny dispositions make yellows good at sales, teaching and entertaining.

DO YOU KNOW YOUR VAMPIRE LORE?

1. Which weapon will never kill a vampire?
   a. Sunlight.
   b. A stake through the heart.
   c. A silver bullet.
2. Count Dracula came from where?
   a. The Carpathian Mountains.
   b. The mountains of Transpennsylvania.
   c. Draculand.
3. Edward Cullen is in love with which girl?
   a. Vicki.
   b. Bella.
   c. Vampirella.
4. There is no such thing as a vampire bat.
   a. True.
   b. False.
5. Which author did not write a book about vampires?
   a. Bram Stoker.
   b. Stephenie Meyer.
   c. Virginia Woolf.

6. A vampire cannot enter your house unless you invite him or her in.
   a. True.
   b. False.
7. Buffy the Vampire Slayer's boyfriend is named . . .
   a. Dirk.
   b. Angel.
   c. Sting.
8. Vampires hate . . .
   a. garlic.
   b. onions.
   c. carrots.
9. Bunnicula is . . .
   a. a nickname for a cute vampire.
   b. a vampire rabbit.
   c. a breakfast snack for vampires.
10. A vampire cannot see his or her reflection in a mirror.
    a. True.
    b. False.

Scoring

Give yourself one point for each correct answer.

1. c
2. a
3. b
4. b
5. c
6. b
7. b
8. a
9. b
10. a

What Your Score Means

9–10 "Count" yourself in as one of Dracula's minions! Avoid bright light and anyone with the last name Van Helsing.

5–8 Practically undead. You know too much about the ways of vampires to be fully human. No wonder your eyes look so bloodshot. Your favourite item of clothing? A cape.

1–4 You possess basic vampire knowledge — enough to potentially save you from dangerous bites. From mosquitoes. Stay in after dark and wear a garlic necklace at all times.

0 You are vampire bait.

HOW WELL DO YOU UNDERSTAND BOYS?

1. You have to buy a birthday present for a boy in your class. You choose . . .
   a. a build-your-own pop bottle rocket kit.
   b. a T-shirt with a skateboarding logo on the front.
   c. a gift card for a video game store.
2. You see three boys sitting together at lunch. You assume they are . . .
   a. eating.
   b. arguing about who is the best all-time hockey player.
   c. making fart jokes.

3. A boy in your class has just said, "Hi!" to you. That means . . .
   a. he likes you.
   b. he hates you.
   c. he likes your best friend.
4. Which of these three movies would a boy most like to see?
   a. *Escape from Explodo-Earth*
   b. *Dog Washington Slept Here*
   c. *Terminatransformers VII*
5. When a boy says, "Cool!" it means . . .
   a. I wasn't listening.
   b. I really like that!
   c. Leave me alone now.

6. Boys like girls who . . .
   a. are feminine and gentle.
   b. are kind.
   c. like the same stuff they do.
7. A boy you like asks you to play one-on-one basketball. You should . . .
   a. decline. Boys are such sore losers.
   b. beat the pants off him.
   c. say, "No, let's just talk."

8. There is one handful of popcorn left in the bowl. You . . .
   a. let the boy you are with have it — you were taught to always be polite.
   b. take it — he would have grabbed it if he'd noticed it first.
   c. tell him to go make some more popcorn.

Scoring

Give yourself 0 points for each A answer. Give yourself 0 points for each B answer. Give yourself 0 points for each C answer.

How You Rate

0–0 What were you thinking? You are a girl! You will never understand boys. They are silly, silly creatures. No matter how hard you try, you will never be able to figure out why they think walloping each other on the arm is fun, or why they seem so completely clueless about all things essential like personal grooming. Just shake your head and get on with the important business of running the world while they snicker at armpit-farts.

WHAT'S YOUR FASHION DIVA STYLE?

1. You would describe yourself as . . .
   a. conservative. You don't like to stand out in a crowd.
   b. the life of the party.
   c. creative and kooky.
   d. one of the gang.
2. Which animal is your favourite?
   a. Dogs.
   b. Cats.
   c. Horses.
   d. Ferrets or iguanas. You can't decide.
3. What is your favourite type of food?
   a. Hot, hotter, hottest — spice is nice!
   b. Simple — nothing too weird or exotic.
   c. Tex-Mex — lots of cheesy goodness!
   d. Vegan — crunchy veggies and lots of interesting flavours.
4. On a vacation, you'd love to . . .
   a. go parasailing.
   b. Paris. Just take me to Paris.
   c. go for a long nature hike.
   d. veg out.
5. What kind of music do you like?
   a. Country.
   b. Pop.
   c. Jazz.
   d. Salsa.

6. Which is your favourite colour?
   a. Black.
   b. Pinks and purples.
   c. Nature colours — browns, greens and blues.
   d. All of them, preferably together!
7. Which would you rather do after school?
   a. Play a game with a friend.
   b. Watch TV with your family.
   c. Read.
   d. Participate in an organized after-school activity with your friends.
8. Which topic do you know the most about?
   a. Your favourite boy band.
   b. Your friends' lives and feelings.
   c. Your favourite TV show or movie characters.
   d. How to get noticed.

Scoring

1. a1 b4 c3 d2
2. a2 b1 c3 d5
3. a4 b1 c2 d3
4. a3 b4 c2 d1
5. a3 b2 c4 d5
6. a1 b3 c2 d4
7. a3 b1 c2 d4
8. a2 b4 c1 d5

You Are . . .

9–16 Plain Jane. You're not the kind of gal who likes to make waves. Keep it simple, you say. Comfy and casual, that's you!

17–24 Sporty Spice. You like to get out there and do it, not just sit on the sidelines. So you prefer clothes with clean lines in stretchy fabrics that look sleek and no-nonsense. Yoga pants in sharp colours are among your fashion faves.

25–29 Chic and cheerful. You love colour, pattern and variety. You love to dress up in fun and funky getups. Lots of pink, lots of hearts and flowers, lots of fun!

30–35 Feather boas and long gloves. You, dahling, have true fashion flair. You are the first with the latest style, the glitziest bling and the best brands. You make your friends drool with diva envy.

WHAT'S YOUR EYE Q?

How good is your spatial sense? Can you figure out puzzles just by looking at them? Find out with this test!

1. What is the next letter in this series?

A B D O P Q ___

2. Look at the picture below. It shows a cube that has been cut apart and flattened.

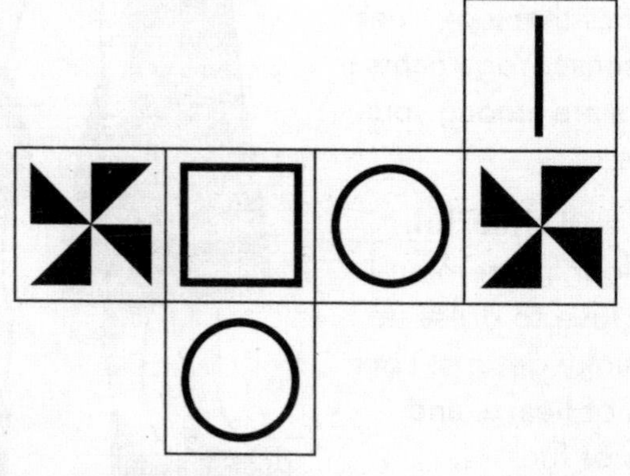

Which of the two cubes shown below will it make if you fold up the flattened cube again?

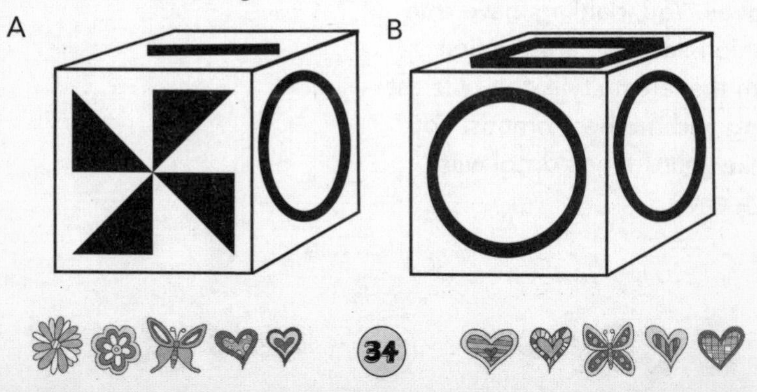

3. How many squares of any size are there in this picture?

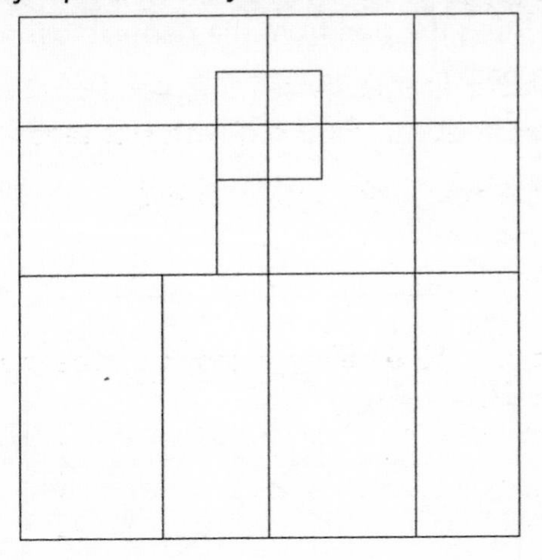

4. How many individual cubes are there in this picture? All rows and columns are complete, unless you can see where they end.

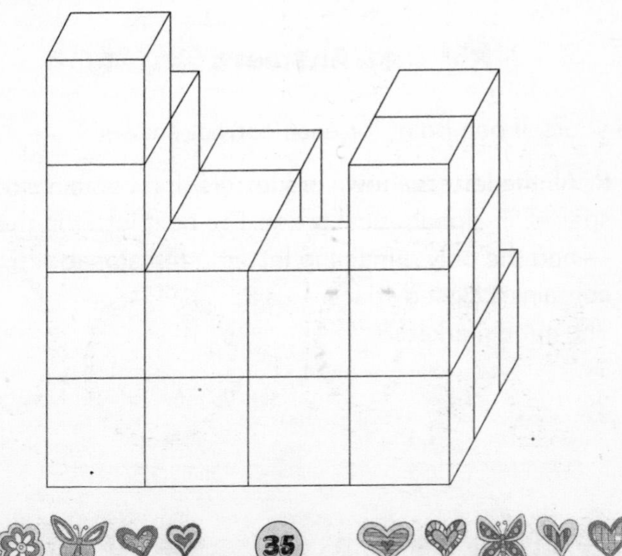

5. Can you draw this picture using a single continuous line, without lifting the pen from the paper, crossing any lines or doubling back?

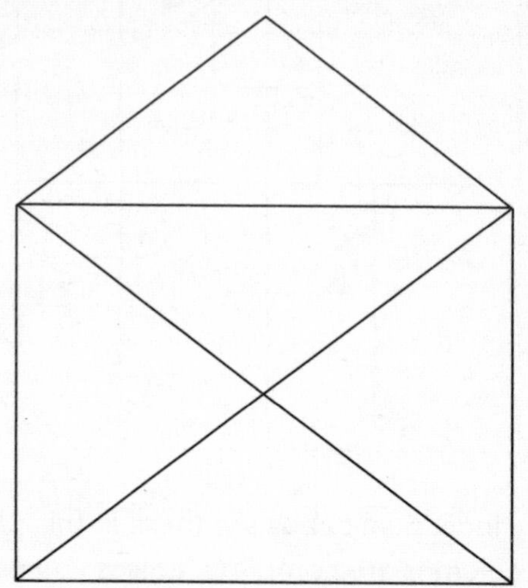

Answers

Give yourself one point for each correct answer.

1. R. All the letters shown are letters that contain closed spaces, in alphabetical order. The next letter in the series — and the only remaining letter in the alphabet that contains a closed space — is R.
2. The cube marked B.
3. 14.
4. 25.

5. Here is one possible solution.

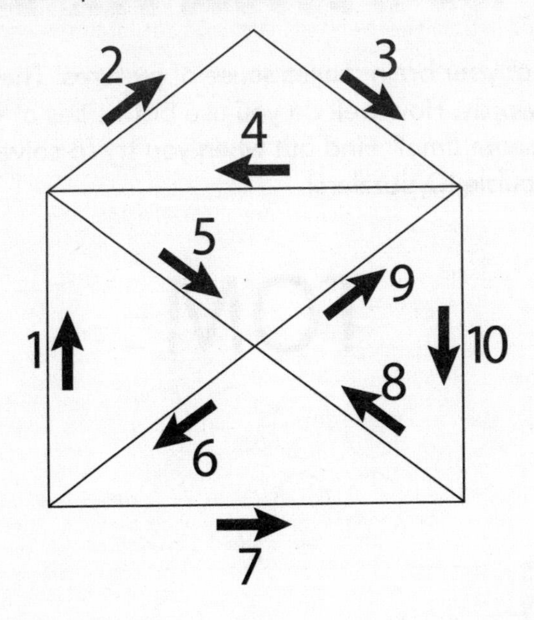

You Are . . .

0 Puzzled by puzzles.

1–2 Very clever.

3 Practically a genius.

4 A real brainiac.

5 Smarter than Einstein!

ARE YOU A DOUBLE BRAINIAC?

One side of your brain makes sense of pictures. The other decodes words. How well do you use both sides of your brain — *at the same time?* Find out when you try to solve these double-trouble IQ puzzlers!

1.

TOM

O O O O
O O O O

2. **PANTS**
PANTS

3. *FOOD*

4.

o o
1 1
O O

5. T I R E

6. F R I E N D S

STANDING
MISS

F R I E N D S

7. One Another
One Another
One Another
One Another
One Another
One Another

8. VIOLETS
VIOLETS
VIOLETS
VIOLETS
VIOLETS
VIOLETS

9.

– – SNOW – –

10.

3 135 72

21 good 988 14

45 48 6 2519

61 57 80

Answers

Give yourself one point for each correct answer.

1. Tomatoes (Tom + eight O's).

2. Pair of pants.

3. Fast food.

4. Dark circles under the eyes.

5. Flat tire.

6. Misunderstanding between friends.

7. Six of one, half a dozen of another.

8. Shrinking violets.

9. Dashing through the snow.

10. Good with numbers.

You Are . . .

0 Puzzled by puzzles.

1–2 Very clever.

3–5 Practically a genius.

6–8 A real brainiac.

9–10 Smarter than Einstein!

WHAT'S YOUR ANIMAL TOTEM?

Many First Nations peoples believe that we each have a personal spirit guide, or totem, that protects us through life. Your totem is usually a kind of animal whose nature reflects your own personality. Find out which animal is your totem and what it means.

1. A classmate teases you. How do you react?
   a. You tease her back. > Go to question 2.
   b. You withdraw and try to fade into the background. > Go to question 3.
   c. You lose your temper and call her names. > Go to question 4.
   d. You shrug your shoulders and walk away — she's not worth worrying about. > Go to question 5.
2. Where do you feel happiest or most comfortable?
   a. In wide-open spaces — where you can see for miles, like the prairie or the beach. > Go to question 6.
   b. In your room — it's personal and cosy. > Go to question 10.
   c. Where the action is — lights, camera, woohoo! > Go to question 7.
3. Which personality trait sounds more like you?
   a. Stubborn. > Your totem is the Tortoise.
   b. Competitive. > Go to question 4.
4. Which activity is your favourite?
   a. Hockey. > Your totem is the Wolverine.
   b. Chess. > Your totem is the Snake.
   c. Gymnastics. > Your totem is the Wolf.

5. You prefer . . .
   a. to hang out by yourself. > Go to question 8.
   b. being with a group of friends. > Go to question 9.
   c. being with your family. > Go to question 11.
6. How would you like to be described?
   a. Smart or wise. > Your totem is the Eagle.
   b. Daring. > Go to question 7.
   c. Powerful. > Your totem is the Polar Bear.
7. Which extreme sport would you prefer?
   a. Surfing. > Your totem is the Whale.
   b. Water skiing. > Your totem is the Sea Otter.
   c. Skydiving. > Your totem is the Raven.
8. Which do you prefer to do when you are on your own?
   a. Climb a tree. > Your totem is the Eagle.
   b. A craft, such as beading or scrapbooking. > Your totem is the Snake.
9. Which do you prefer?
   a. Meat and potatoes. > Your totem is the Wolf.
   b. Fish. > Your totem is the Whale.
   c. Shellfish. > Your totem is the Sea Otter.
   d. Vegetables. > Your totem is the Deer.
10. What is your favourite time of year to be off from school?
   a. Snow days rock! > Your totem is the Polar Bear.
   b. Summer vacation rules! > Your totem is the Tortoise.
   c. You fall for Thanksgiving. > Your totem is the Wolf.
11. You prefer . . .
   a. three square meals a day. > Your totem is the Wolverine.
   b. to snack all day long. > Your totem is the Deer.
   c. to try new foods. > Your totem is the Raven.

What Your Animal Totem Means

Deer. You are a natural athlete — fleet of foot and graceful. You are a bit shy but can overcome that tendency as long as you have a friend or two with you. Your strengths include highly tuned senses, gentleness, honesty and integrity. Your weakness is a tendency to worry.

Eagle. You tend to be imaginative, with a wide range of interests and abilities. You are fiercely independent and don't like others to tell you what to do. Your strengths are speed, a talent for languages and excellent vision. Your weakness is difficulty empathizing with others.

Polar Bear. You tend to be cool, calm and collected, unless something irritates you. Then watch out! Your strengths include stamina, intelligence and courage. Your weaknesses are stubbornness and irritability.

Raven. You are smart, talkative and easily distracted. You are very active and energetic, with a daring streak and a love of luxury. Your strengths include a talent for making others laugh and solving complex problems. Your weaknesses include a tendency to gossip and waste time.

Sea Otter. You are friendly and fun-loving. Your strengths include superior social skills and a joyful attitude that makes others feel good. Your weakness is a desire to avoid unpleasantness at all costs.

Snake. You love to do things that others consider unusual — perhaps going to a natural history museum or a concert of classical music? Your strengths include patience, keen intelligence and flexibility. Your weaknesses include timidity and greed.

Tortoise. You are a solid, steady and reliable friend and teammate. You think things through carefully and logically and are therefore not easily swayed by the crowd. You have a strong sense of right and wrong and never veer from your chosen path. Would some go so far as to call you "stubborn"? Stranger things have happened.

Whale. You are good at almost everything you do and have an enormous appetite for life. You love to travel. Your strengths include a talent for sports (especially water sports) and communication. Your weakness is difficulty settling down — you may find it hard to focus on homework or stick with a sport.

Wolf. You are very outgoing, loyal, trustworthy and a good team member. When it's time to get down to work, you roll up your sleeves and pitch in. Your strengths include a good sense of humour, empathy and friendliness. Your weakness is a tendency to go along with the crowd.

Wolverine. You are a fierce competitor. A lack of sleep or food can cause you to lose your temper over any little thing. Your strengths include a passionate nature, intensity and a complete indifference to obstacles. Your weakness is a tendency to lash out at others.

ARE YOU A BORN LEADER?

1. Halloween is coming soon. You and your friends agree it would be fun to have a party. What happens next?
   a. Your friends look to you to get things organized.
   b. Nothing. You trick or treat with your best pal, just like always.
   c. You go to the party and help get things set up.
2. Your soccer team is behind, 2–1, at halftime. What do you do?
   a. Get depressed.
   b. Encourage everybody to get back in the game and give it their all, then get back on the field in an upbeat mood with a newly energized team.
   c. Play even harder in the second half. Someone has to get the job done!

3. In class . . .
   a. you rarely ask questions — you hate having people think you are a teacher's pet.
   b. you frequently ask questions that the teacher has trouble answering — you like to dig deep into new subjects.
   c. you ask just enough questions to get a good mark for participation.

4. You are thinking about going for your bronze medallion in swimming. It will be a tough challenge for you and you're not sure you can do it. What are you most likely to do?
   a. Sign up but miss half the practices. You probably wouldn't have passed the test anyway.
   b. Go for it! You thrive on pushing yourself.
   c. Forget about it. It will be too hard.
5. Your teacher offers you the chance to help mentor younger kids in reading. Your performance will be reviewed by other kids in your class. What will you do?

   a. Volunteer. You'll enjoy doing the work, plus it will be good to learn to get feedback — good or bad — from your classmates. You want to learn.
   b. Opt out. You don't feel comfortable in new situations.
   c. Opt out. You'd just crumble if you got a bad review from your friends!
6. Would you consider yourself trustworthy?
   a. Absolutely.
   b. Sometimes. You try to be but you can be forgetful.
   c. Not sure.
7. Your class is choosing a class president. Which is most likely?
   a. You put your own name forward and your friends support you.
   b. Your name won't come up as an option.
   c. You will definitely be put forward — you're a natural spokesperson and people know that about you.

8. Your teacher asks your opinion about an event in the news. What will happen next?
   a. Your classmates listen respectfully — they know you will have something interesting and worthwhile to say.
   b. You clam up.
   c. You say the first thing that comes to your mind.

Scoring

1. a3 b1 c2
2. a1 b3 c2
3. a1 b3 c2
4. a2 b3 c1
5. a3 b2 c1
6. a3 b2 c1
7. a2 b1 c3
8. a3 b1 c2

What Your Score Means

8–13 Team player. You usually prefer to let others make the big decisions. When you feel passionate about a subject, however, you can be a persuasive and effective leader.

14–19 Lead on, Macduff! You have strong leadership skills. Others look up to you. Remember to follow through on projects you begin, and you'll increase your leadership potential.

20–24 Alpha dog. You are the undisputed leader of the pack! You are the kind of person other people feel inspired by — confident, knowledgeable, and with a can-do attitude that's infectious.

ARE YOU A GOOD LISTENER?

1. Your mom is telling you about her day. You . . .
   a. ask questions and make comments.
   b. tune her out.
   c. keep playing your video game. You can listen to her at the same time.

2. When your friend is telling you a story, you . . .
   a. jump in with a similar story of your own.
   b. twiddle with a piece of hair or doodle. You listen best while your hands are occupied.
   c. look her in the eye and nod now and then to let her know you are hearing and understanding what she is saying.
3. You tell your friend you don't want to switch camps to join her at the one she goes to — you are happy at your own camp. She crosses her arms and says, "Fine." What does she really mean?
   a. That's A-okay with her.
   b. She's upset with you.
   c. She doesn't really want you at her camp anyway.

4. When people in a group are talking, you tend to . . .
a. interrupt and take over the conversation — you get so excited about the topic, you can't help getting involved in the discussion.
b. worry about what you should say when it's your turn.
c. add a comment that's on topic when there's a gap in the conversation.
5. You are making a poster for a school project with a partner. Your partner wants to do the poster a certain way, but you think that's a bad idea. You . . .
a. ask her to explain her idea, then try to incorporate her suggestions in the final design.
b. cut her off and do the poster your way — it's just a waste of time to listen to her dopey ideas.
c. pretend to listen to her suggestions while in your mind you plan what the poster will really look like.
6. Your teacher explains to you why you got a poor mark on a book report. While she talks, you . . .
a. don't hear a word. You are struggling to hold back tears.
b. ignore her. She's just mean anyway.
c. try hard to understand what she is saying by asking questions and repeating what she says back to her to make sure you got it right.
7. Your neighbourhood friend has just introduced you to some of her school chums. What do you do?
a. Sit quietly and listen to them talk among themselves until you get a better sense of their personalities.
b. Immediately tell them all about yourself. Getting to know new people is fun!
c. Ask them lots of questions about themselves.

8. You are taking your very first guitar lesson. You're nervous. When the teacher tells you how to strum a chord, you . . .
   a. have a hard time following what she says. You're too nervous to listen well!
   b. nod a lot, then do it the way your friend showed you.
   c. look her in the eye, follow her instructions and ask her for feedback (e.g., "You mean strum it like this?")

Scoring

1. a1 b3 c3
2. a2 b3 c1
3. a3 b1 c2
4. a2 b3 c1
5. a1 b3 c4
6. a2 b3 c1
7. a2 b3 c1
8. a2 b3 c1

What Your Score Means

8–15 Hear! Hear! You are interested in what other people say and make an effort both to make sure you understand them properly and to show them you are paying careful attention. As a result, people like to share their thoughts and feelings with you. Your superior listening skills make you a valued friend and top-notch team member.

16–21 Hey! Over hear! Like most people, you sometimes get distracted when you are listening to others. As a result, you occasionally miss what is being said or get information wrong. You can improve your listening skills by making eye contact with the speaker. Just meeting her eyes will help keep you focused and show her you care about what she is saying.

22–25 Say what? Do nerves keep you focused on your own thoughts and feelings? Or do you just have so much to say yourself that you forget to give other people a chance to talk? Both of these listening gaffes are very common. It's easy to become a better listener, though. Just practise these simple techniques: Ask the speaker plenty of questions to help you understand what she is saying. Repeat the speaker's words back to her to show her you were listening and to make sure you understood her correctly. If you find you're not really listening anymore because you are busy thinking about what you are going to say next, refocus and ask the speaker to repeat what you missed. You'll have plenty of time to say your piece once your friend has had her turn, and she'll be more likely to listen to you if you've listened carefully to her.

WHAT ANCIENT CLASSICAL HEROINE OR GODDESS ARE YOU?

1. Which adjective describes you best?
   a. Impulsive. > Go to question 2.
   b. Cool-headed. > Go to question 3.
   c. Open-minded. > Go to question 4.
2. Which do you prefer?
   a. Ponies. > Go to question 5.
   b. Unicorns. > Go to question 6.
3. Which describes you better?
   a. You're a bit of a homebody. > Go to question 10.
   b. You love learning new things. > Go to question 11.
4. Do you like to travel to new and different places?
   a. Yes. > Go to question 9.
   b. No. > Go to question 7.
   c. Sometimes yes, sometimes no. > Go to question 12.
5. Your favourite sport is . . .
   a. hiking. > Go to question 7.
   b. sailing. > Go to question 4.
6. Which describes you best?
   a. You have a wild imagination. > You are Cassandra.
   b. You adore drama and theatre. > You are Hera.
   c. You're a big hugger — you love everybody! > Go to question 12.

7. Which appeals to you more?
   a. Camping in a wild, untamed national park. > You are Artemis.
   b. Visiting historic gardens overflowing with gorgeous flowers. > You are Demeter.
8. Which statement do you agree with more?
   a. Two heads are better than one. > You are Athena.
   b. Home is where the heart is. > You are Helen of Troy.
9. Which movie would you rather see?
   a. Any of the Harry Potter movies. > You are Circe.
   b. A romantic comedy or drama. > You are Penelope.
10. You are more of an . . .
   a. extrovert. > Go to question 8.
   b. introvert. > Go to question 9.
11. You are . . .
   a. an optimist by nature. > You are Cassandra.
   b. a pessimist by nature. > You are Circe.
12. You would describe yourself as . . .
   a. a real people person. > You are Helen of Troy.
   b. a nature girl. > You are Demeter.

You Are . . .

Artemis, Goddess of the Hunt. You're the outdoorsy type. You love animals, flowers, anything that lives and grows. You enjoy sports and being active. No one ever accused you of being a couch potato! Your favourite foods: Venison and wild strawberries.

Athena, Goddess of Wisdom. You know the difference between the important things in life (friends, family, making the world a better place) and stuff that's just silly (greed, envy). You are one smart cookie. Your motto: Think it through.

Cassandra, the Seer. You have a knack for understanding people and their feelings. As a result, you can predict what's going to happen next with uncanny accuracy. Your instincts are usually correct, so listen to them and trust your intuition. Your natural talent: Photography or cinematography.

Circe, the Sorceress. You work your magic on everyone you meet in the form of friendliness and limitless charm. You are a natural diplomat — persuasive, witty and funny when you need to be, but firm and unbending if a situation requires it. Avoid pork.

Demeter, the Earth Goddess. You care a lot about the Earth and about keeping our planet healthy and green. You do your part with a can-do attitude that inspires others. Your favourite foods: Pomegranates and truffles.

Helen of Troy. Your beauty is more than skin-deep — you are a kind, loving person inside and out. Alas, even though you don't mean to be, you're also something of a troublemaker, always in the thick of the action. You sometimes have difficulty making decisions. Your motto: Who, me?

Hera, the Queen Goddess. You are the diva goddess of Olympus with an operatic temperament. All your emotions come in superhuman sizes — including jealousy! Keep in mind that with your divine talents outshining everyone around you, jealousy is wholly unnecessary. You're the queen, after all. Avoid Golden Delicious apples.

Penelope, the Loyal One. You are a super friend — loyal, trustworthy, the kind of pal you can count on when times are tough. But you're no doormat. You know how to influence others and make sure you get your way. Your natural talents: Knitting, weaving and needlework.

HOW FIT ARE YOU?

Are you superhero tough or marshmallow material? We come in all different shapes and sizes, but it's always important to be fit. Being fit helps you get through the day with more energy. It also makes you feel great.

To find out how you stack up, do each of these tests. Then combine your scores in the summary table at the end of this section to get an overall fitness total.

Note: If you are not familiar with these activities, or if you do not exercise regularly, do these tests with adult supervision.

Test 1, Upper Body Strength — The Push-Up

You will need:
A friend
A stopwatch or clock with a second hand

To do a push-up, lie face down on the floor. Put your palms on the floor just below your shoulders. Keeping your body straight (like a plank) push into the floor with your arms to raise yourself off the floor. Do not arch your back or bend your knees.

Do as many push-ups as you can in one minute, without losing the proper form.

Scoring

Use the number of push-ups you did to determine your score. If you're younger than 10, add 2 to your total for every year you're under 10. For example, if you are 9 years old and did 5 push-ups, add 2 to your total to give you a score of 7.

Look at the chart below to determine your final score. Put that score in the summary table at the end of these tests.

Less than 7 Needs improvement.	Put a 4 in the summary table.
7–14 Good on ya! Healthy fitness achieved!	Put a 6 in the summary table.
15–20 High fives! High fitness level!	Put an 8 in the summary table.
21+ Superstar athlete!	Put a 10 in the summary table.

Test 2, Upper Body Strength — The Flexed-Arm Hang

You will need:
A friend
A stopwatch or a clock with a second hand
A chin-up bar or other horizontal bar

To do a flexed-arm hang, begin by hanging from the bar using an overhand grip (so the palms of your hands face away from you). Keep your chest close to the bar. Maintain this position as long as you can. Stop timing when 1) your chin touches the bar, 2) your head tilts back (to keep from touching the bar) or if 3) your chin falls below the level of bar.

Scoring

Start with the number of seconds you held your position. Look at the chart below to determine your final score. If you are younger than 10, add one to your score in the chart.

Put that score in the summary table at the end of the tests.

Less than 4 seconds Needs improvement.	Put a 4 in the summary table.
4–9 Good on ya! Healthy fitness achieved!	Put a 6 in the summary table.
10–18 High fives! High fitness level!	Put an 8 in the summary table.
More than 18 seconds Superstar athlete!	Put a 10 in the summary table.

Test 3, Core Strength — The Sit-Up

You will need:
A friend
A stopwatch or a clock with a second hand

To do a sit-up, lie on your back with your hands clasped on the back of your neck and your fingers touching or interlaced. Bend your knees and put the soles of your feet on the floor. Your heels should be no more than 30 cm from your bum. Curl up your torso until your elbows touch your knees. Then lower yourself back down. Be sure not to pull on your neck with your hands — they are not there to pull you up. Do as many sit-ups as you can in one minute.

Scoring

Start with the number of sit-ups you did. If you are older than 10, subtract 2 for every year you are older. If you are younger than 10, add 2 to your number.

Look at the chart below to determine your final score. Put that score in the summary table at the end of the tests.

Less than 32 Needs improvement.	Put a 4 in the summary table.
32–39 Good on ya! Healthy fitness achieved!	Put a 6 in the summary table.
40–47 High fives! High fitness level!	Put an 8 in the summary table.
48+ Superstar athlete!	Put a 10 in the summary table.

Test 4, Aerobic Fitness — Run in Place

You will need:
A friend
A stopwatch or a clock with a second hand

To do the test, run in place, jump rope or do jumping jacks for three minutes. At the end of the three minutes, describe how you feel.

Scoring

Look at the chart on the next page to determine your final score. Put that score in the summary table at the end of the tests.

Stopped before the 3 minutes were up. Needs improvement.	Put a 4 in the summary table.
Heart pounding, exhausted. Getting there.	Put a 6 in the summary table.
A little breathless but okay. High fitness level.	Put an 8 in the summary table.
Barely broke a sweat. Superstar athlete!	Put a 10 in the summary table.

Test 5, Balance Test — Standing on One Leg

You will need:
A friend
A stopwatch or clock with a second hand

Close your eyes. Lift one foot off the floor by bending your knee. Remain standing on one foot as long as possible. Repeat two more times. Then do the test three times on the other foot.

Scoring

Use your best time for scoring.

Look at the chart below to determine your final score. Put that score in the summary table at the end of the tests.

Less than 12 seconds Weeble	Put a 4 in the summary table.
12–23 seconds Dreidel	Put a 6 in the summary table.
24–29 seconds Stork	Put an 8 in the summary table.
More than 29 seconds Rock	Put a 10 in the summary table.

Summary Table

Test	Score
Test 1	
Test 2	
Test 3	
Test 4	
Test 5	
Total	

Overall Score

Add up your scores from each of the five fitness tests. Compare your total to the scores here.

20–29 Gear grinder. You would benefit from more activity in your day. It's important to find something you like — maybe being part of a team would get you out more. Soccer, softball and hockey are all great games. Or maybe you'd prefer something more solitary like running or bike riding. Get active for at least ten minutes at a time, four times a day.

30–39 Primed for action. Your fitness level is good. You can build strength and stamina by playing a wider variety of sports and practising your skills every day. Work up a sweat for at least twenty minutes, three times a day to increase your fitness power.

40–50 Star athlete. You've got excellent strength and stamina. Build on this solid base by increasing the time you engage in physical activity to an hour or more every day. You'll excel in any sport you work at.

ARE YOU DOUBLE-JOINTED?

Being double-jointed does not mean you have an extra joint in any part of your body. The term refers to a joint that is more flexible than is typical in most people. Many people have a few joints that are unusually flexible. But not as many are extremely flexible in many joints.

Answer yes or no to the following questions:

1. Can you touch your left thumb to the inside of your left wrist?

2. Can you touch your right thumb to the inside of your right wrist?

3. Can you straighten your arms so that your elbows point in instead of out?

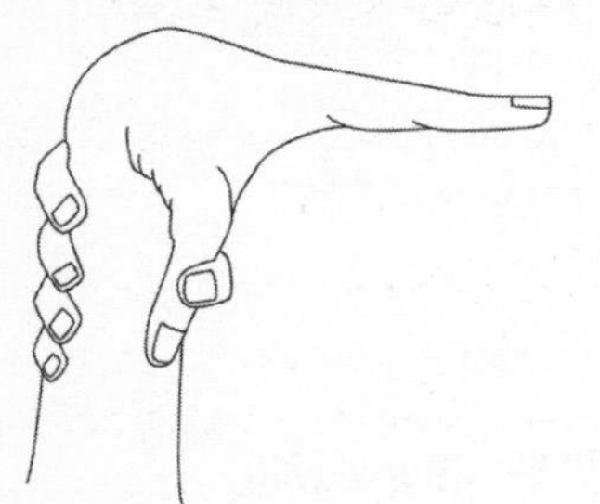

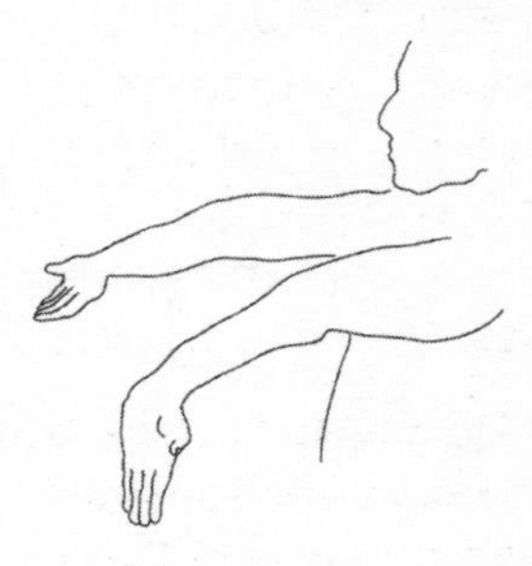

4. Can you straighten your legs so your knees flex backwards?

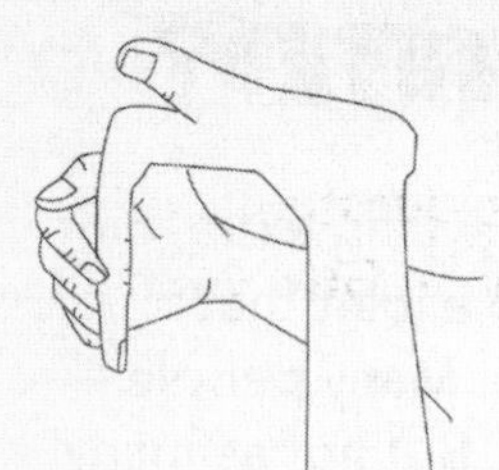

5. Can you bend the four fingers on your right hand so they flex backwards?

6. Can you bend the four fingers on your left hand so they flex backwards?

7. Can you flex your right ankle up at an extreme angle?

8. Can you flex your left ankle at an extreme angle?

9. Can you bend just the top joint of any one finger, while the rest of the finger is straight?

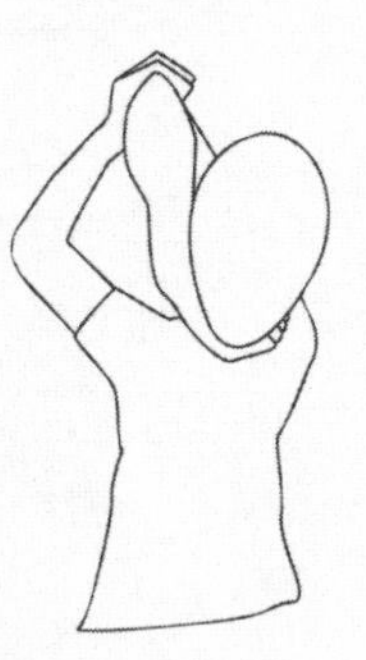

10. Can you stretch your arms above you and wrap one around your neck?

11. Can you wrap either leg around your neck?

12. Can you twist or bend any other joint in your body in an unusual or extreme way?

Scoring

If you answered yes to one or more of these questions, it means that the joint in question is very flexible. Give yourself a point for each yes answer.

Results

2–4 Double trouble! You can freak out your friends with your extreme joint sports.

5–8 Rubber-band gal! You are extremely twistable and twisted.

9–12 Contortionist! Have you considered a career in the circus?

ARE YOU LEFT BRAINED OR RIGHT BRAINED?

Your brain is divided into two halves. Each half is somewhat specialized to do different tasks. While we all use both sides of our brains to think and function, most people tend to rely on one side of the brain more than the other. We say that side of the brain is "dominant."

The dominant side of the brain affects your personality, likes and dislikes and thinking style. Take this quiz to find out which side of your brain is dominant and what that says about you.

Answer yes or no to each question.

1. I always like to know what time it is.
2. I find following directions can be tricky.
3. I see the world in pretty clear terms — things are black or white, not grey.
4. I prefer not having to follow a strict schedule.
5. When I lose something, I try to picture it in my head to figure out where I last saw it.
6. When I give directions, I like to draw a map of how to go.
7. Doing addition, subtraction or other math skills is a snap.
8. I listen to my hunches.
9. When I get something new, I always like to read the directions on how to use it or how to put it together.

10. When I'm thinking about the answer to a question, I turn my head to the left.
11. I think I'd make a great detective because I'm good at details.
12. I'm very musical.

13. If someone asks me a question, I usually look up and to the right.
14. When I have to solve a problem, I usually think about similar problems I have solved in the past.
15. If I'm trying to remember a person's name and I can't, I go through the alphabet until I remember it.
16. I believe there is always more than one way to look at almost everything.
17. I write with my right hand.
18. I frequently lose track of time.
19. When I climb stairs, I put my right foot on the step first.
20. I wave my hands around a lot when I talk.

Scoring

Add up the number of YES answers you gave for the ODD-numbered questions (1, 3, 5, etc.): _______

Add up the number of YES answers you gave for the EVEN-numbered questions (2, 4, 6, etc.): _______

If you have more yeses for the odd-numbered questions, you are more likely left brained. More yeses for the even-numbered questions means you are more likely right brained.

If You Are . . .

Left brained:
You tend to be logical and detail-oriented, with a preference for facts, facts and more facts. You prefer subjects like math or science that have clear-cut, right or wrong answers and rely on order and sequence. You can be very practical, and you are good at coming up with effective strategies for getting the job done.

Right brained:
You are very creative. You tend to see the big picture and think all the little details are boring and petty. You love to make up stories, imagine crazy and funny scenes or draw and paint. You also have a great sense of humour and get along well with other people. You rely on your instincts and hunches, and your gut feelings are usually right.

ARE YOU AN INNIE OR AN OUTIE?

Are you a shy introvert or an outgoing extrovert? This surprisingly simple test reveals secrets about your mind's basic nature.

What to do: Using the index finger of your dominant hand (the hand you write with), trace the capital letter Q on your forehead.

Analysis

You could have "drawn" the Q in either of two ways:

If you drew the Q with its tail pointing to your left — so the Q would look normal to an observer "reading" the letter if it really appeared on your forehead — you are an extrovert.

If you drew the Q with its tail pointing to your right — so the Q would look backwards to an observer "reading" the letter if it really appeared on your forehead — you are an introvert.

If You Are . . .

An extrovert:

You care a great deal about other people and make an effort to see things from their point of view. You enjoy being around other people and get energy from them. You are good at understanding other people's feelings and make an empathetic and caring friend.

An introvert:

You tend to be a private type of person and look inward for creative inspiration. You have strong and consistent values and are not easily swayed by others. You are very honest and forthright and make a loyal and trustworthy friend.

WHAT DO YOUR HANDS SAY ABOUT YOU?

Scientists know that a hormone called testosterone circulates through everyone's bodies. Boys and men have more of it than girls and women, but it is essential to female health and functioning, too.

The amount of testosterone circulating in a mother's body before her baby is born can affect how its brain develops. That, in turn, may affect its personality. Even more surprising, scientists say testosterone-linked personality traits may be predicted by examining the lengths of your fingers! That's because testosterone also affects finger growth in an unborn baby.

What to do?

1. Hold out your right hand, palm up, with your fingers as shown.
2. Compare the length of your index finger (marked 1 in the illustration) with your ring finger (marked 2 in the illustration).
3. Which is longer, your index finger or your ring finger?

Analysis

If your index finger is longer, or about the same length as your ring finger, you were probably exposed to typical levels of testosterone in the womb. Some of these "Low-T" traits may apply to you: collaborative, passive, caring, easy-going, patient.

If your ring finger is longer than your index finger, you were probably exposed to higher levels of testosterone in the womb. Some of these "High-T" traits may apply to you: competitive, assertive, logical, leader, impatient.

HOW ARTSY ARE YOU?

Are you artsy? Or do you prefer the beauty of logic and numbers? Try this simple test to reveal your brain's secret preference.

What to do:

1. Clasp your hands together, interlocking your fingers.
2. One thumb will naturally wind up on top of the other. Which thumb is it?

If it is your RIGHT thumb: You're a numbers gal!

If it is your LEFT thumb: You're artsy!

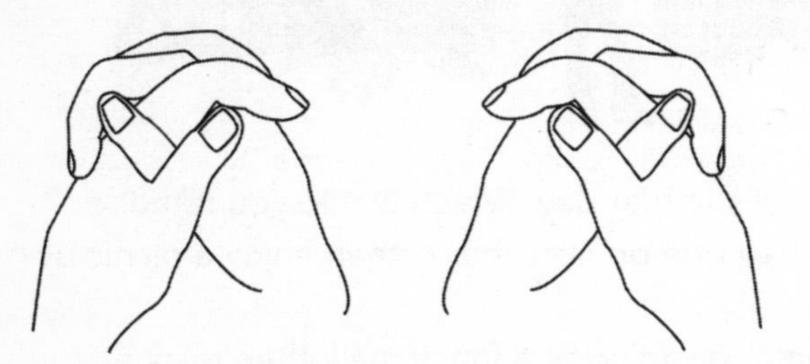

What? You don't believe it? Try this follow-up test: Fold your arms across your chest. Which arm ends up on top? If it's the same as in the thumb test, then your brain's preference is confirmed. If it's the opposite, consider yourself lucky! You combine the best of both the artistic and the logical personality types.

ARE YOU A CITY GIRL OR A COUNTRY GIRL?

1. It's a beautiful summer day. Which would you rather do?
   a. Go for a trail ride on horseback, then enjoy a picnic by a stream.
   b. Spend time shopping at a fancy mall, then relax at an outdoor cafe for lunch.
   c. Go to a just-released movie.
2. Which sporting event would you go to?
   a. Monster truck pull.
   b. Major league baseball game.
   c. Your local Little League game.
3. Which food sounds yummiest?
   a. Oysters on the half shell.
   b. Corndog.
   c. Submarine sandwich.

4. Which chore would you rather do?
   a. Help weed a garden.
   b. Clean out your closet.
   c. Run out and buy a newspaper for your dad.
5. Your ideal outfit includes . . .
   a. a cute black skirt.
   b. overalls and a trucker hat — in pink.
   c. a swimsuit.
6. Where would you prefer to go on your next family vacation?
   a. The beach or a cottage.
   b. New York City.
   c. Camping in Alberta.
7. A "sty" is . . .
   a. a pen for pigs.
   b. a thingy you get in your eye.
   c. a cool abbreviation for "stylish."
8. Baby animals are . . .
   a. so cute!
   b. a lot of work.
   c. the perfect fashion accessories.
9. When you grow up, you want a job that . . .
   a. lets you spend a lot of time outdoors.
   b. is full of glamour and excitement.
   c. doesn't involve sitting at a desk all day.
10. Which sounds like the scariest movie?
   a. *The Farmhouse*
   b. *The Elevator*
   c. *The Woods*

Scoring

1. a1 b2 c3
2. a1 b3 c2
3. a3 b1 c2
4. a1 b2 c3
5. a3 b1 c2
6. a2 b3 c2
7. a1 b2 c3
8. a2 b1 c3
9. a1 b3 c2
10. a3 b1 c2

You Are a . . .

11–18 Country girl. Keep your big-city traffic, fancy-pants fashions and noise, noise, noise! You like the laid-back rural life — since life's simple pleasures are the best.

19–25 Suburbanite. You like variety — a little bit of this and a little bit of that. Why be forced to choose when you can have the best of both worlds?

26–30 City girl. You thrive on action, action and more action. No wonder you crave city life — it's as exciting as you are.

HOW GREEN ARE YOU?

1. When you brush your teeth . . .
   a. you let the water run while you brush.
   b. you turn off the water so you don't waste it.
   c. You avoid brushing your teeth as often as possible.
2. Recycle means . . .
   a. use something over again.
   b. bike to school.
   c. send used material back to a place where it can be taken apart and made into something new.

3. What are the three Rs?
   a. Reduce, Reuse, Rewrite.
   b. Reading, Writing, 'Rithmetic.
   c. Reduce, Reuse, Recycle.
4. To use less energy, what should you do?
   a. Turn off the lights when you are not using them.
   b. Use fans instead of air conditioning.
   c. Both a and b.
5. Which kind of foods do you usually eat?
   a. Fast food.
   b. Organically grown fruits and vegetables.
   c. I don't care — whatever is on my plate.
6. To save water, what should you do?
   a. Take a shower instead of a bath.
   b. Take a bath instead of a shower.
   c. Turn down the temperature on your water heater.

7. How do you get to school?
   a. A school bus picks me up.
   b. My parents drive me.
   c. I walk or ride my bike.
8. When you bring a lunch to school . . .
   a. you use disposable sandwich bags, disposable forks or spoons and throw all the waste in the garbage.
   b. you use paper bags and other wrappers that can be recycled.
   c. you use a lunchbox and reusable containers that can be washed.
9. Hand-me-down clothes are . . .
   a. gross.
   b. not stylish enough for me.
   c. a smart idea — you use fewer resources when you reuse clothes and reduce the number of things you buy.
10. Which do you use the most?
   a. TV or MP3 player.
   b. Video game console or computer.
   c. Soccer ball or skateboard.

Scoring

1.	a1 b3 c2	6. a3 b0 c1
2.	a2 b1 c3	7. a1 b0 c3
3.	a0 b0 c3	8. a0 b1 c3
4.	a1 b1 c4	9. a0 b0 c3
5.	a0 b5 c2	10. a1 b1 c5

You Are a . . .

4–10 Olive drab. You are not very environmentally aware or concerned. It's time to realize that the choices you make DO make a difference. Help take care of your planet!

11–20 Moss green. You do a few good things to help protect our planet. Add a few more simple activities, such as turning off lights when you leave a room and spending more time playing active games instead of ones that use electricity. You'll help the planet and feel great, too!

21–27 Spring green. You are doing a lot to help keep the planet healthy. Keep up the good work and continue trying new ways to save energy and waste fewer resources.

28–35 Bright green. You are a green giant! You make the three Rs an everyday part of your life. Spread the news to make your great green spirit go even further. The planet thanks you!

WHAT KIND OF COOKIE ARE YOU?

1. Your favourite symbol is . . .
   a. a smiley face. > Go to question 2.
   b. a rainbow or unicorn. > Go to question 3.
   c. a skull. > Go to question 4.
2. Which would you enjoy more?
   a. Going fishing. > Go to question 5.
   b. Building a tree house. > Go to question 6.
3. You prefer . . .
   a. a bath. > Go to question 7.
   b. a shower. > Go to question 8.
4. When you doodle, you draw . . .
   a. people. > Go to question 9.
   b. lines, squares and other shapes. > Go to question 10.
5. Which makes you angrier?
   a. People treating you badly. > You are a Sugar Cookie.
   b. People treating other people badly. > You are a Chocolate Chip Cookie.
6. Which appeals to you more?
   a. High tea at a hoity-toity hotel. > You are Classic Shortbread.
   b. Watching jugglers and mimes at a street art festival. > You are a Macaroon.
7. Which patterns do you prefer?
   a. Pinstripes or polka dots. > You are a Brownie.
   b. Hearts and flowers. > You are a White Chocolate Chunk Cookie.
8. In a group, you tend to . . .
   a. be the listener. > You are an Oreo.
   b. be the talker. > You are a Chocolate Chip Cookie.

9. You prefer . . .
   a. slapstick humour. > Go to question 10.
   b. shaggy dog stories and tall tales. > You are a Macaroon.
10. Your favourite subject is . . .
    a. math or science. > You are an Oatmeal Raisin Cookie.
    b. art or music. > You are a Ginger Snap.

What Your Cookie Says About You

Brownie. You loooove the good life and dream of fancy designer clothes, glamorous vacations in far-off hot spots, having "staff." You enjoy indulging your senses with things like bubble baths, flavoured lip gloss and luxurious fabrics like fake fur and satin. Warning: You are vulnerable to flattery.

Chocolate Chip. Good-natured, easy-going, you take life in stride and don't let obstacles stand in your way. In fact, you enjoy the bumps along the road of life — for you, they represent adventure, excitement and fun! You are well liked and are a welcome part of any team.

Classic Shortbread. You are pared down and elegant, with the kind of natural style others try to copy but can never duplicate. That's because there's nothing phoney about you — you believe in the good old-fashioned value of kindness and practise what you preach.

Ginger Snap. You are a true individual. You march to your own drummer, follow your own star. You think that being true to yourself is what brings spice to life and that differences are to be celebrated, not feared.

Macaroon. You're a little bit wacky — in a good way! You think the world needs to laugh more and you're the one to make 'em do it! Your motto: Life is fun!

Oatmeal Raisin. You have sophisticated tastes. You love sinking your teeth into a problem and finding novel solutions. You recognize that life is full of challenges and that not everyone will agree with your view of things. You are logical and level-headed.

Oreo. You are conservative but sometimes surprise others with your twisted thinking. You frequently see the world as either black or white. You tend to hide your true feelings. You're sweet at heart.

Sugar Cookie. Keep those fancy dolled-up cupcakes — they often look better than they taste. You like to keep things simple and pure. Just the facts, please. People like your straight-up honesty and lack of airs. You can be trusted. In certain situations, you really sparkle.

White Chocolate Chunk. Go big or go home is your motto! Are your friends going rock climbing? You'll tackle Everest. Jumping rope for charity? You'll hop till you drop. Your enthusiasm is catching. You inspire others with your passion for life.

ARE YOU A DRAMA QUEEN?

1. You broke a nail. What do you do?
   a. Scream, cry and rant.
   b. Stop what you are doing and go and fix it. You can't possibly be seen with that horror!
   c. Bite off the ragged edge and get on with what you were doing.
2. Your best friend likes the same boy you do. You . . .
   a. never speak to her again.
   b. get in a huge fight and draw all your other friends into whose side they are on.
   c. laugh about it — he doesn't notice either one of you!
3. You have a test coming up in science. The night before, you . . .
   a. study and kick back for a while — you are relaxed and confident.
   b. stay up late studying — you get really, really nervous before tests!
   c. panic and freak out — you HAVE to get a good grade on this test or else your life will be over!
4. Two of your friends are in a fight. You . . .
   a. steer clear — they'll work things out between themselves.
   b. get the low-down from both of them — you have to know what's going on all the time!
   c. shuttle back and forth between them, telling one what the other has said.

5. You've just seen a really sad movie. What happens next?
   a. You get totally involved in the story. It upsets you so much, you can't sleep or you have nightmares.
   b. You feel sad for a while but then get over it and move on.
   c. You call up your friends and tell them how AWFUL you feel after watching such a HEARTBREAKING movie.
6. Which career sounds like it would suit you best?
   a. EMT or ambulance driver — you thrive on action.
   b. Movie star.
   c. Clown.
7. Which shoes suit the inner you the best?
   a. Super high heels — high fashion all the way!
   b. Running shoes.
   c. Flip-flops.
8. You've just been chosen class valedictorian! You . . .
   a. scream at the top of your lungs and jump up and down.
   b. smile and blush.
   c. feel a nice warm glow wash through you.
9. You've been invited to a party that you really want to attend, but your parents have said you can't go! You . . .
   a. scream, throw things and slam doors.
   b. try to explain to them why the party means so much to you.
   c. scream, throw things, slam doors AND you complain bitterly to all your friends about how horrible your life is and that your parents are the worst in the whole world.
10. Your everyday mood is . . .
    a. totally unpredictable! You're all over the map — up, down, you name it!
    b. generally happy.
    c. generally pessimistic.

Scoring

1.	a5 b3 c1				6.	a3 b4 c2
2.	a4 b5 c1				7.	a5 b2 c1
3.	a1 b3 c5				8.	a5 b2 c1
4.	a1 b3 c5				9.	a3 b1 c5
5.	a3 b1 c4				10.	a5 b1 c3

You Are . . .

11–20 Mary Poppins. You are easy-going and take most life events in stride. Nothing really ruffles your feathers, for good or bad. Sometimes, you even wonder what all the fuss is about!

21–30 Miley Cyrus/Hannah Montana. You are a little bit of this and a little bit of that. Sometimes, you're just a kid who likes to hang with your family and play with your stuffies. But other times, you're a can-do gal who wants to step out and own the spotlight! One second, you can feel calm, cool and collected, but then SNAP! You get spinny and feel completely out of control of your emotions. In other words, you are perfectly normal.

31–40 Scarlett O'Hara. You feel things intensely and people around you know it! Your enthusiastic response to everything that happens in your life makes you exciting and fun to be with.

41–48 Ready for Broadway! You live life at the highest levels of intensity. Yes, you ARE a total drama queen. That means that for you, life is never, ever boring. But at the same time, your passionate nature can leave you feeling drained and exhausted. Don't forget to take time to smell the flowers to keep yourself calm and centred. That way, you can enjoy the excitement of being in the limelight without burning yourself out.

ARE YOU BFF MATERIAL?

Answer each question true or false.

1. I have lots and lots and *lots* of pals.
2. I think loyalty and honesty are important qualities.
3. I really enjoy hanging out and gossiping with my friends.
4. I most enjoy doing fun activities with my friends, like sports or crafts.
5. I sometimes get jealous of my friends' accomplishments.
6. Being part of the cool crowd isn't something that matters much to me.
7. If someone tells me a secret — oops! — I have a habit of spilling the beans.
8. I feel happy and excited when something nice happens to one of my friends.
9. I like to know things that other people don't — knowledge is power, after all!
10. I have known one or more of my friends ever since we were babies!
11. I don't want my best friend to have other close friends that might take her away from me.
12. I tend to get along well with everybody.
13. I expect people to do what I ask them to do and to agree with my opinions.
14. People trust me with their feelings.
15. I get cross when I don't get my way.
16. If a friend upsets me, I will tell her — but I'll try to do it gently.
17. I sometimes blurt things out before I think them through — foot-in-mouth disease!

18. I tend to behave the same way with all kinds of people — I'm just my ordinary self.
19. Being popular is important to me.
20. I judge people by their personalities, not by the clothes they wear or stuff they have.

Scoring

Add up your FALSE answers for all the ODD-numbered questions. _______

Add up your TRUE answers for all the EVEN-numbered questions. _______

Add the two totals together for your score. _______

How You Rate

0–3 Trust rust. You find it difficult to open up to people and be yourself. You tend not to trust others and treat them differently than you like to be treated. True friendships are based on mutual respect — let people get to know you better, and you'll reap the rewards of better and deeper friendships.

4–9 Green queen. You can be a great friend until — uh-oh! — jealousy rears its ugly head! Build up your own skills and self-confidence so you can be a loyal supporter of your pals without turning green with envy. That's what will make you your buddy's BFF.

10–16 Mellow yellow. People like you because you are easy to get along with and don't give off lots of attitude. Be discreet with private information and avoid spreading rumours or indulging in other catty behaviour. Soon everyone will want to be your BFF!

17–20 True blue. You are true BFF material — loyal, honest and caring. You have a realistic appreciation for how hard it is to maintain a friendship. You are a good listener. You aren't easily swayed by peer pressure to do or say things that aren't true to your own nature or that would betray a friend.

HOW WELL DO YOU KNOW CANADA?

1. Canada has how many provinces and territories combined?
   a. 10
   b. 12
   c. 13
   (Can you name them?)
2. There is a rainforest and a desert in Canada.
   a. True
   b. False
3. The longest highway in Canada is called . . .
   a. the Cross-Canada Highway.
   b. the Chilkoot Trail.
   c. the Trans-Canada Highway.
4. How long is the US–Canada border?
   a. 12,280 km
   b. 8,890 km
   c. 5,280 km
5. The largest Canadian island in a freshwater lake is called . . .
   a. Winnipeg Island.
   b. Manitoulin Island.
   c. Vancouver Island.
6. Which Canadian city is not a UNESCO World Heritage Site?
   a. Montreal.
   b. Lunenburg.
   c. Quebec City.

7. Which is the longest river in Canada?
   a. The Mackenzie River.
   b. The Nahanni River.
   c. The St. Lawrence River.
8. The Canadian Shield is . . .
   a. part of Canada's coat of arms.
   b. part of Canada's geography.
   c. a play used in Canadian football.
9. Where is the southernmost point of the Canadian mainland?
   a. In Nova Scotia.
   b. At the The British Columbia–Washington state border.
   c. In Ontario.
10. When did Nunavut become a territory?
    a. 1899.
    b. 1957.
    c. 1999.
11. The North Magnetic Pole is in Canada.
    a. True
    b. False
12. Which is Canada's national animal?
    a. The moose.
    b. The beaver.
    c. The polar bear.
13. Which city is the largest in Canada?
    a. Toronto.
    b. Montreal.
    c. Vancouver.
14. Which province joined Canada last?
    a. Newfoundland.
    b. British Columbia.
    c. Nunavut.

15. Canada is the largest country in the world.
    a. True
    b. False
16. How many time zones are there in Canada?
    a. 4.
    b. 6.
    c. 8.
17. The kayak, the canoe and the Ski-Doo are all Canadian inventions.
    a. True
    b. False
18. The first prime minister of Canada was . . .
    a. Mackenzie King.
    b. Sir Alexander Mackenzie.
    c. Sir John A. Macdonald.
19. Canada's birthday is . . .
    a. July 4
    b. July 14
    c. July 1
20. "The Mounties" is a nickname for Canada's national police force. What is their official name?
    a. Canada's Mounted Royal Police.
    b. The National Canadian Mounted Police.
    c. Royal Canadian Mounted Police.

Scoring

Give yourself 1 point for each correct answer. Add an extra point to your total if you named all ten provinces and all three territories correctly.

1. c. The provinces are Alberta, British Columbia, Manitoba, New Brunswick, Newfoundland and Labrador, Nova Scotia, Ontario, Prince Edward Island, Quebec and Saskatchewan. The territories are Northwest Territories, Nunavut and Yukon.
2. a. Both are in British Columbia!
3. c
4. b
5. b
6. a
7. a
8. b
9. c. It is in Point Pelee National Park.
10. c
11. a
12. b
13. a
14. a. Newfoundland joined Confederation in 1949. Its name was changed to Newfoundland and Labrador in 2001. Nunavut is a territory.
15. b. It is the second largest.
16. b
17. a
18. c
19. c
20. c

You Are a . . .

0–5 Voyageur. You've embarked on an exciting journey of discovery, learning about this great country we call home. Lucky you! There's still so much more fun stuff to learn. Paddle on, fur trader!

6–12 Nation builder. You've got a solid foundation in Canadiana. But don't stop there — you can add a second storey, you know.

13–17 Future MP. You sure know a lot about Canada — more than enough to please politicians, diplomats and social studies teachers across this great nation!

18–20 Future prime minister. You surely are a Canadian know-it-all. No wonder you are destined for national leadership.

21 Captain Canada. How *do* you know so much about this country? Are you actually a moose in disguise?

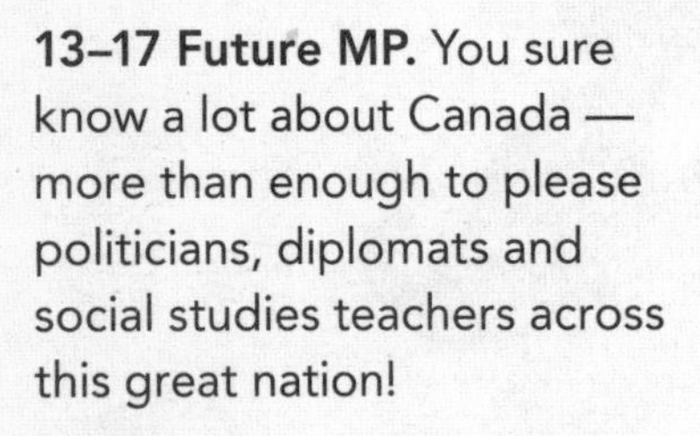

WOULD YOU RATHER . . .

1. eat a live worm or a dead caterpillar?

2. be stranded on an island with no water or risk drowning on the open ocean during a hurricane?
3. give a speech in front of five thousand people or sing a cappella by yourself in front of fifty people?
4. be bitten by a poisonous snake or mauled by a bear?
5. wash five thousand dishes or mow five hundred lawns?
6. lose your sense of taste or vision in one eye?

7. face a shark or an angry bull?
8. jump from a plane or climb Mount Everest?
9. have too many children or no children?
10. wake up as a dog or an octopus?